Out of this World

PEACE
FORCE

by Sally Odgers
pencils by Matt Lin
inks by Aaron Lin

S P   R T S

First published in 2007
by Macmillan Education Australia Pty Ltd.

Text by Sally Odgers
Pencils by Matt Lin
Inks by Aaron Lin
Cover Design Allison Parry
Design by Matt Lin/Goblin Design
Managing Editor Nicola Robinson

Out of this World: Peace Force
ISBN 978 1407 10180 4

Printed by Tien Wah Press, Singapore

1 2 3 4 5 6 7 8 9   9 0 1 2 3 4 5 6 7 8

Contents

Three kinds of people live on Space Station Nova.

The Stationborn have been there for generations.

The Prof

Luke

Janna

Coach

The Shipborn were born on giant spaceships that wander the Galaxy.

The Earthborn came to Nova from Earth.

Pavros

Ellie

There has always been rivalry between the three sets of Stationers but one thing brings them together: the game they call 3D.

The team is on top form as shipborn Janna Troubadour, Gold Saver, launches her best move.

Luke's grandfather, Prof, and his dog, Breezeblock, are happy.

THE TEAM EMERGES FROM THE DOME ...

THE CAPTAIN IS EARTHBORN ... FAVOURITISM ... IT'S A STATION TEAM.

WHAT'S GOING ON?

IT LOOKS BAD ...

SUDDENLY ...

YOU SHOULDN'T BE PLAYING WITH THEM.

LET ME GO!

SLAP!

OOF!

GOT YOU! WHAT RIGHT HAS AN EARTHBORN TO CAPTAIN A STATION TEAM?

- 10 -

PROF SWITCHES HIS SCANNER TO SPEAKER MODE.

LISTEN TO THIS!

PEACE FORCE APPROACHING. READY TO LOCK ON.

WHAT'S GOING ON?

MAYOR KLIKWITZ HAS CALLED IN SOME BACKUP.

THAT'S GOOD ... ISN'T IT?

GOOD? THIS IS MAD K'S FAULT! BIRTH PRIDE IS FINE, BUT HE PUTS THE EARTHBORN IN CHARGE OF EVERYTHING!

ATTENTION, HUMANS!

WHAT DO THEY MEAN, HUMANS?

MAYOR KLIKWITZ COMES TO GREET PEACE FORCE.

ON BEHALF OF SPACE STATION NOVA, I—

I'LL BRIEF YOU— HEY!

TROOPS! SECURE THIS STATION.

BACK IN PROF'S WORKSHOP, EVERYONE WATCHES IN HORROR ...

THAT'S IT! I'M GOING TO DEAL WITH MAD K AND THESE NUTS IN HELMETS!

COACH

- 18 -

PROF WATCHES AS GENERAL LORK AND HIS PEACE FORCE SECURE NOVA.

WHAT'S GOING ON, PROF?

LOOKS LIKE MAD K HAS MET HIS MATCH.

IT'S NOW SO COLD THE STATIONERS CAN SEE THEIR OWN BREATH ...

... AND THE TEMPERATURE CONTINUES TO DROP.

IT'S SO COLD! I HAVEN'T BEEN THIS COLD SINCE WE LEFT EARTH.

IT DOESN'T MAKE SENSE.

IS SOMETHING WRONG WITH THE THERMO-LEVEL?

I CAN SEE WHY THESE PEOPLE CUT THE GRAVITY, BUT WHY THE TEMPERATURE CHANGE?

WHERE'S BREEZEBLOCK? HE WAS HERE JUST NOW.

HE'S GONE TO THE SECRET ROOM. HE'S LEARNED TO OPEN THE TRAPDOOR.

SECRET ROOM?

SUDDENLY—

BAM!

PROF HAS CLOSED THE HATCH!

QUICK, THE SCANNER! SOMETHING MUST HAVE HAPPENED.

LUKE FOCUSES THE SCANNER.

THEY'VE ROUNDED EVERYONE UP.

WHY HAVEN'T PROF AND THE COACH COME DOWN?

CAN YOU SEE ANY OTHER PLACES?

I CAN HEAR SOMETHING ...

UP ABOVE ...

ANYONE ELSE HERE?

CAN YOU SEE ANYONE?

WE'RE NOT RIOTING, SO LEAVE US ALONE.

chapter 3 : Aliens

THE TEAM BEGINS TO MAKE PLANS.

THAT'S WHY IT'S COLD. THE ALIENS MUST COME FROM A COLD PLANET WITH LOW GRAVITY.

GROAN. I HATE THE COLD.

LUKE HAS AN IDEA.

I KNOW! WE CAN USE 3D TACTICS.

BOMB THEM WITH BALLS?

FIND OUT THEIR WEAKNESSES –

– AND EXPLOIT THEM.

THE TEAM BEGINS TO MAKE PLANS.

THEY DON'T LIKE OUR GRAVITY, OR OUR TEMPERATURE, SO THEY CHANGED IT.

LET'S RESET THE CONTROLS AND CHANGE IT BACK.

BUT THE CONTROLS ARE ON THE GRAVITY LEVEL. THEY'LL CATCH US IF WE GO OUT.

AND THEY TOOK THE SPACE-SKIPPER.

IN KLIKWITZ'S OFFICE, THE ALIENS MAKE THEMSELVES AT HOME.

I'LL GET SOME OF THE TROOPS TO FIX THE SLEEPING RACKS IN HERE.

THE HUMAN SLAVES CAN DO IT.

THE PEACE FORCE PUT SOME CAPTURED STATIONERS TO WORK.

THE LEG WEIGHTS WILL ALLOW YOU TO MOVE AS IF THERE WERE GRAVITY.

PROF AND COACH MERIWETHER FASTEN SLEEPING RACKS TO THE WALL.

COACH

LOOKS AS IF THEY SLEEP UPSIDE DOWN.

NO TALKING. HURRY UP.

BACK IN THE SECRET ROOM...

IF THOSE ARE FOR SLEEPING, THEY MUST SLEEP LIKE BATS.

WHAT?

EARTH ANIMALS. YOU SHIPBORN WOULDN'T KNOW THEM.

LET'S SEE WHAT ELSE IS GOING ON IN THE STATION.

THERE'S THE GRAVITY CONTROL ROOM.

BUT WE CAN'T GET THERE TO USE IT!

WE CAN HANDLE OURSELVES IN LOW GRAVITY. IT'S LIKE PLAYING 3D.

BUT SO CAN THE ALIENS.

THERE MUST BE SOMETHING WE CAN DO ... WAIT! I HAVE AN IDEA!

HUH?

WHERE'S BREEZEBLOCK DO YOU THINK HE COULD GET TO THE MAYOR OFFICE?

AND DO WHAT?

WELL, PROF SAID HE CAN OPEN DOORS. MAYBE HE CAN ALSO CARRY A NOTE.

A NOTE TELLING THE PROF ABOUT OUR PLAN TO SAVE NOVA AND THAT HE AND COACH SHOULD BE READY TO HELP!

AND THE ALIENS PROBABLY WON'T NOTICE A DOG WALKING ABOUT! BRILLIANT!

BREEZEBLOCK, HERE BOY! PHWEEEEP!

HE'S ASLEEP.

SNORT— SNUFFLE— SNERF!

CAN SOMEONE WAKE HIM WHILE I WRITE MY NOTE?

BREEZEBLOCK, TIME TO WAKE UP BOY.

WOOF?

LUKE WRITES A QUICK NOTE AND SENDS BREEZEBLOCK UP THE GRAVITY-CHUTE.

UP, BOY. FIND PROF. GOOD BOY.

PAV, WATCH THE SCANNER, AND TELL ME WHEN HE GETS TO PROF. THEN PROF WILL KNOW WE'RE WORKING ON THIS PROBLEM.

THE PROF ...

... WHY NOT BEEP HIM?

BECAUSE THE ALIENS WOULD NOTICE THAT FOR SURE! NOW BE QUIET. I NEED TO FIND SOMETHING ...

IT'S GOT TO BE SOMEWHERE.

LUKE SEARCHES A STORAGE LOCKER.

IF YOU TOLD US WHAT YOU'RE LOOKING FOR, WE COULD HELP.

REMEMBER THAT BLANKOUT PROF USED TO HAVE?

THAT STUFF THAT MAKES THINGS INVISIBLE?

LUKE HAS LEFT THE SECRET ROOM. NOW HE STALKS TWO ALIENS.

I NEED TWO DIRECT HITS!

WAM!

BAM!

GOAL!

HEY, ELLIE, CAN YOU GUYS COME UP HERE AND GIVE ME A HAND?

LUKE WANTS US TO GO OUT INTO THE CORRIDOR.

WELL, I CAN'T SEE THE ALIENS THERE.

LET'S GO!

MOMENTS LATER IN THE CORRIDOR.

SO YOU KNOCKED THEM OUT WITH THE 3D BALLS?

IT WAS JUST LIKE GOAL PRACTICE.

OK, LET'S TAKE THEM TO THE WORKSHOP AND I'LL TELL YOU THE REST OF MY PLAN.

- 34 -

WITH JANNA AS THEIR 'PRISONER', PAV AND ELLIE SEARCH FOR FREE STATIONERS.

SEEN ANYONE, PAV?

NO, IT'S PRETTY QUIET.

HANG ON, WHAT'S THAT OVER THERE?

SOME STATIONERS HAVE ESCAPED THE ALIENS ...

HELP ME! PLEASE, ANYONE HELP ME!

... BUT THEY'RE NOT KEEN TO HELP EACH OTHER.

SOUNDS LIKE SOMEONE'S IN TROUBLE.

OVER HERE!

NO! SHE'S EARTHBORN!

HUH, WHAT'S THIS?

WHY'D WE STOP?

PLEASE HELP ME!

QUICK ... CAN WE GET TO HER?

NOOOO! SHE'LL GIVE US AWAY!

THERE'S ONE!

I'LL GET HER!

OUCH!

YOU OK?

PAV, HE JUST DROPPED ME!

PLEASE DON'T ... PLEASE ...

'CAUSE SHE'S EARTHBORN...

HEY! SO AM I.

PAV, I THINK I HEAR SOMEONE COMING.

JANNA, YOU AND HER HIDE. ELLIE, GRAB THE GUY!

QUICK – PRETEND TO BE OUR PRISONERS.

COME ON, YOU!

HAH! WHAT'S GOING ON HERE?

COME ON, HUMAN. LET'S GO.

FOUND SOME MORE HUMAN VERMIN? GREAT. DO YOU NEED ANY HELP?

NO, WE'RE GOOD.

OK. SEE YOU AT PROCESSING.

PHEW, THAT WAS CLOSE.

AND YOU TWO, STOP BEING SO STUPID OR WE'LL END UP AS SLAVES TO ALIENS.

COME ON, WE'LL SEE WHO ELSE WE CAN FIND.

WE'RE ALL STATIONERS, RIGHT?

GUESS SO. OK.

I WONDER HOW LUKE'S GOING?

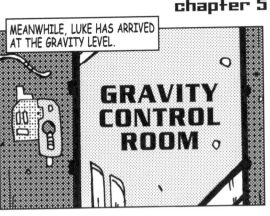

MEANWHILE, LUKE HAS ARRIVED AT THE GRAVITY LEVEL.

GRAVITY CONTROL ROOM

NOW FOR THE TRICKY BIT.

LUKE CREEPS UP BEHIND THE PRISONERS.

PSSSST. THE GRAVITY WILL COME BACK. BE READY.

WHA—?

NOW FOR THE GRAVITY AND TEMPERATURE CONTROLS.

THAT'S BETTER.

WHAT? WHO? I'M GOING TO GET YOU!

OOPS! ONE GUARD LEFT!

YOU DON'T LIKE OUR STATION? NOW YOU DON'T HAVE TO SEE IT

HA, HA, A QUICK TWIST OF YOUR HELMET AND ... VOILA!

ARGH! I CAN'T SEE!

LUKE REVEALS HIMSELF.

QUICKLY, EVERYONE. NET THESE ALIENS. THEN GUARD THAT LEVER.

HEY, HE'S FROM GOLD TEAM JUNIOR! HE'S THAT STATIONBORN KID.

WHO CARES WHAT HE IS? HE'S TALKING SENSE.

... UM YOUR FOOT IS IN MY MOUTH.

- 43 -

ON THE GRAVITY LEVEL, THE STATIONERS HAVE FOLLOWED LUKE'S COMMANDS.

NO ALIEN WILL GET PAST US, RIGHT? WE'RE STATIONERS!

YEAH! STATIONERS!

MEANWHILE BACK IN MAYOR KLIKWITZ'S OFFICE ...

IF I WAS OUT OF THIS NET I'D ...

HAH!, YOU'RE IN THERE AND I'M OUT HERE! DON'T FORGET YOUR PLACE, SLAVE!

WHA—?

OOOF!

THANKS FOR STOPPING MY FALL, FELLA! SO, COACH, STILL THINK THE KIDS CAN'T HELP?

COACH

SOMEONE HAS DONE SOMETHING!